Boffin Boy and the Lost Yeti
by David Orme

Illustrated by Peter Richardson

Published by Ransom Publishing Ltd.
Radley House, 8 St Cross Road, Winchester, Hants. SO23 9HX
www.ransom.co.uk

ISBN   978 178127 048 6
First published in 2013
Copyright © 2013 Ransom Publishing Ltd.

Illustrations copyright © 2013 Peter Richardson

Design & layout: *redpaperdesign.co.uk*

Find out more about Boffin Boy at *www.ransom.co.uk.*

Boffin Boy
AND THE
Lost
Yeti

By David Orme

Illustrated by Peter Richardson

Ransom

Boffin Boy and Katt are going mountain climbing in Scotland ...

They reach the top …

… and decide to go down again.

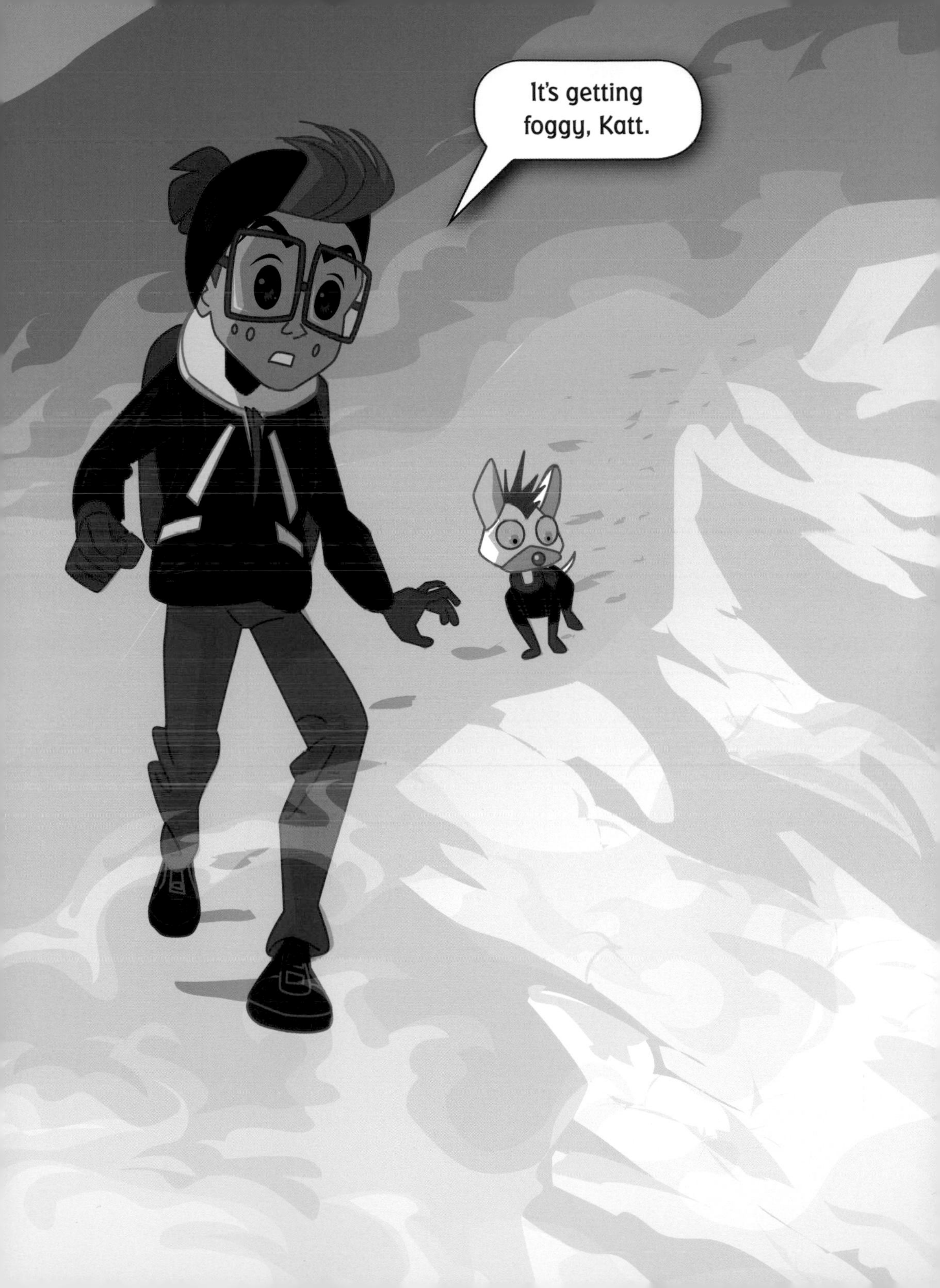
It's getting foggy, Katt.

Watch out, Boffin Boy! There's a great big hairy thing behind you!

It's a yeti! What's that doing in Scotland?
It's probably on holiday, like us!
Good job I've got my camera.
GZZZTTTT

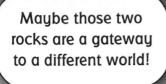

The team decide to check it out ...
Katt can sense something strange!
It's probably Boffin Boy's socks.

I'm picking up something strange, too. Something is wrong with space and time here!

So where are we, Boffin Boy? Is this a different world?
No, this is our world. But thousands of years in the future.

We have travelled in time!
Trust Boffin Boy to leave the sandwiches behind.
I'm hungry! Hurry up with that Lizard, Wu Pee!

So when are we going back to our time?
Er … there's a bit of a problem about that. The gate in time has closed.
You mean we'll have to wait until it opens again?
At least there are lots of lizards.

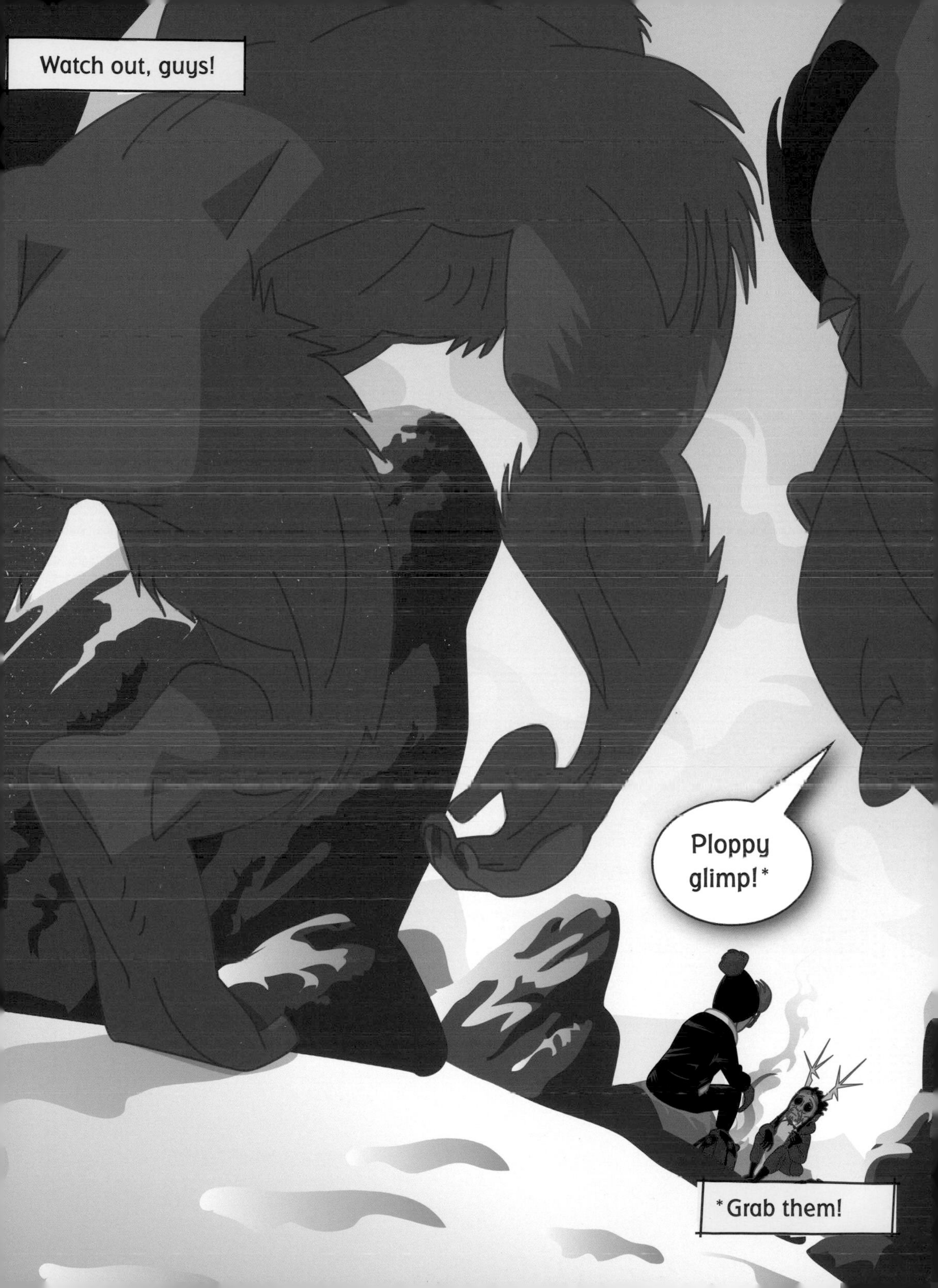
Watch out, guys!
Ploppy glimp!*
*Grab them!

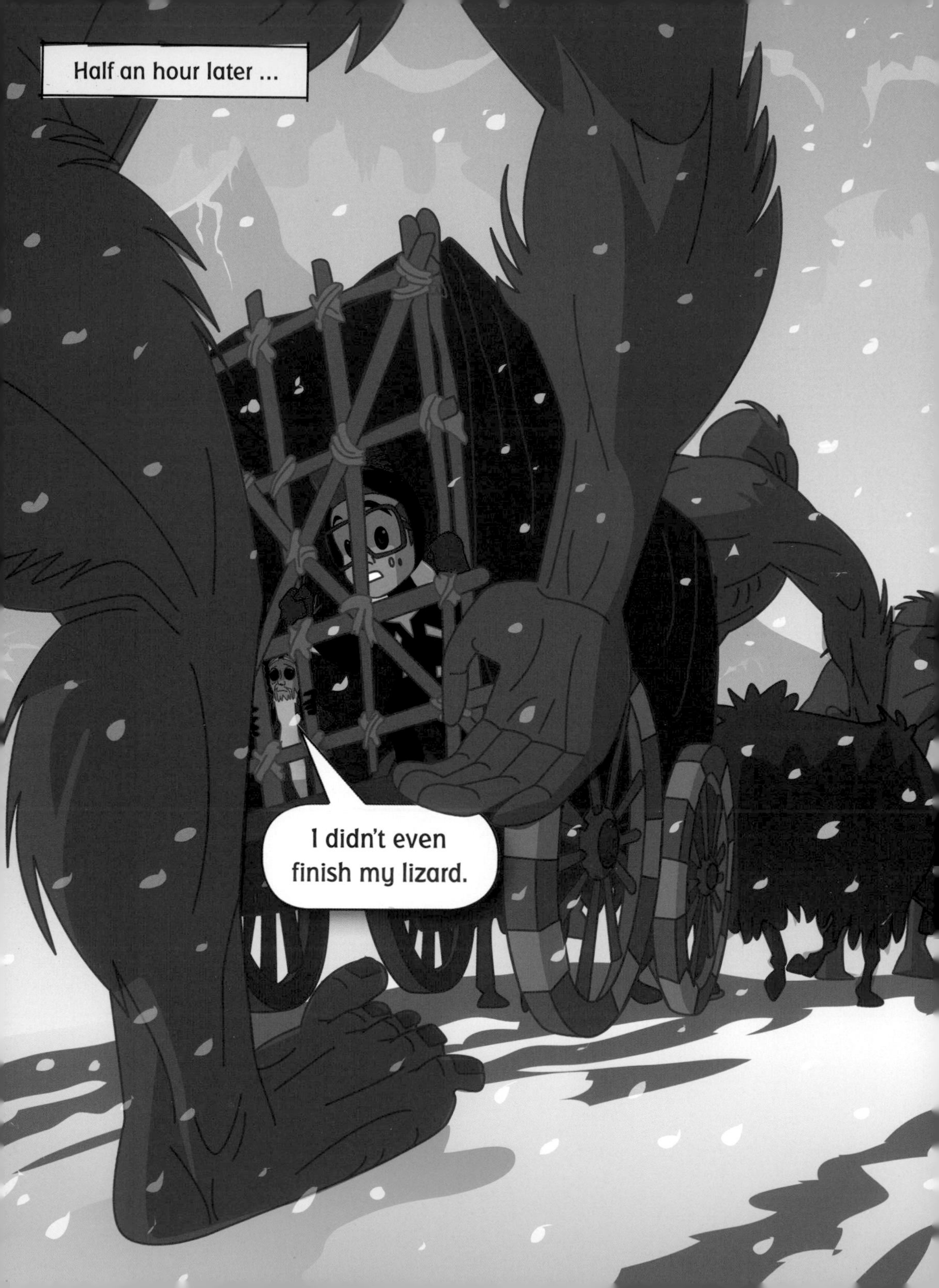
Half an hour later ...
I didn't even finish my lizard.

So what happened to human beings, then?
Maybe they have turned into yetis.

So how do they end up coming back to our time?
There's a crack in time, Wu Pee. They wander through by accident.

So how does that work then?
Well, there's these little tiny stringy things, and one end is in the past, and one end is in the future …
So your theory is, it's all done by strings?
Yep. It's called string theory.
Don't worry about it, Wu Pee.

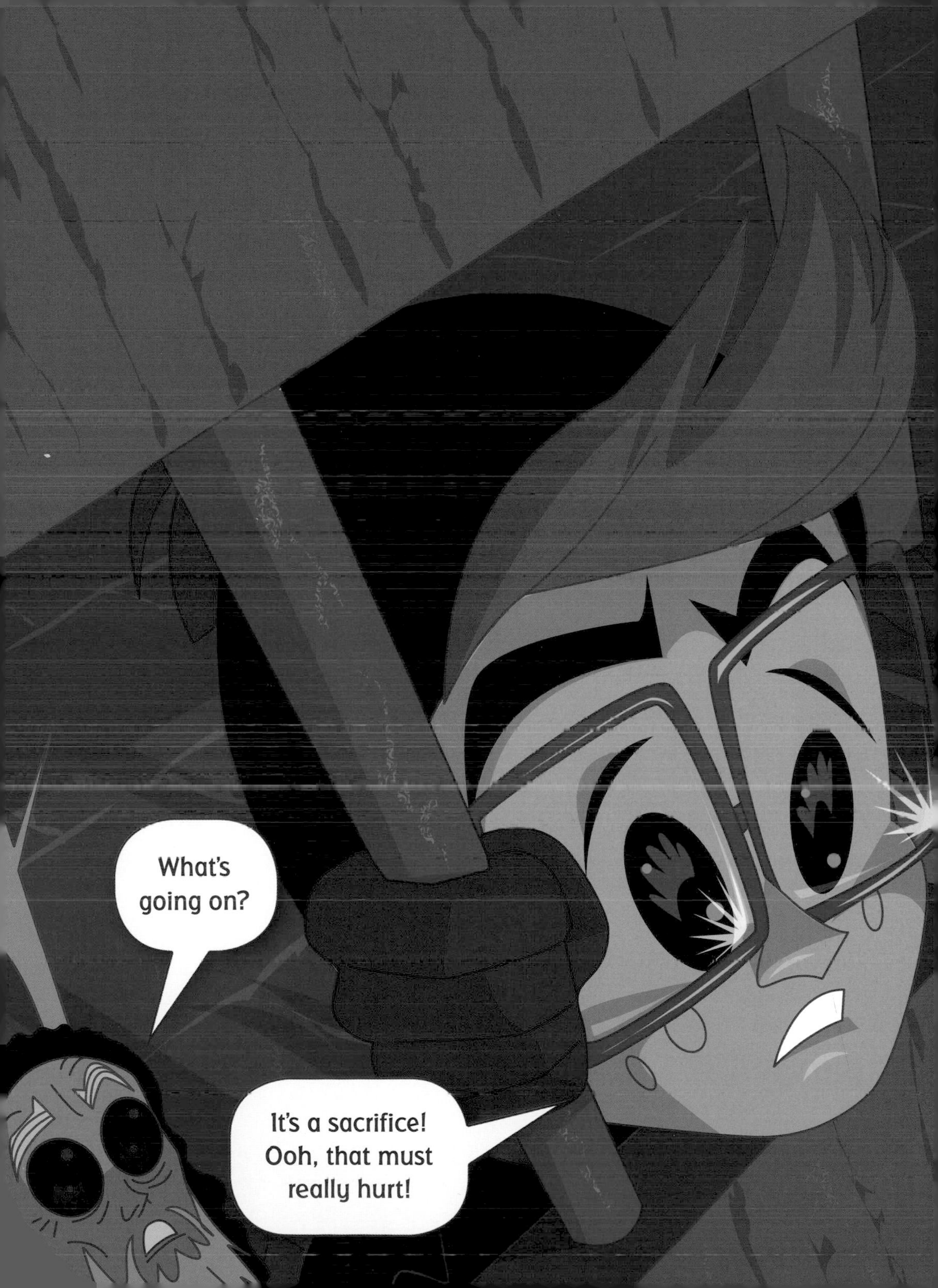
What's going on?
It's a sacrifice! Ooh, that must really hurt!

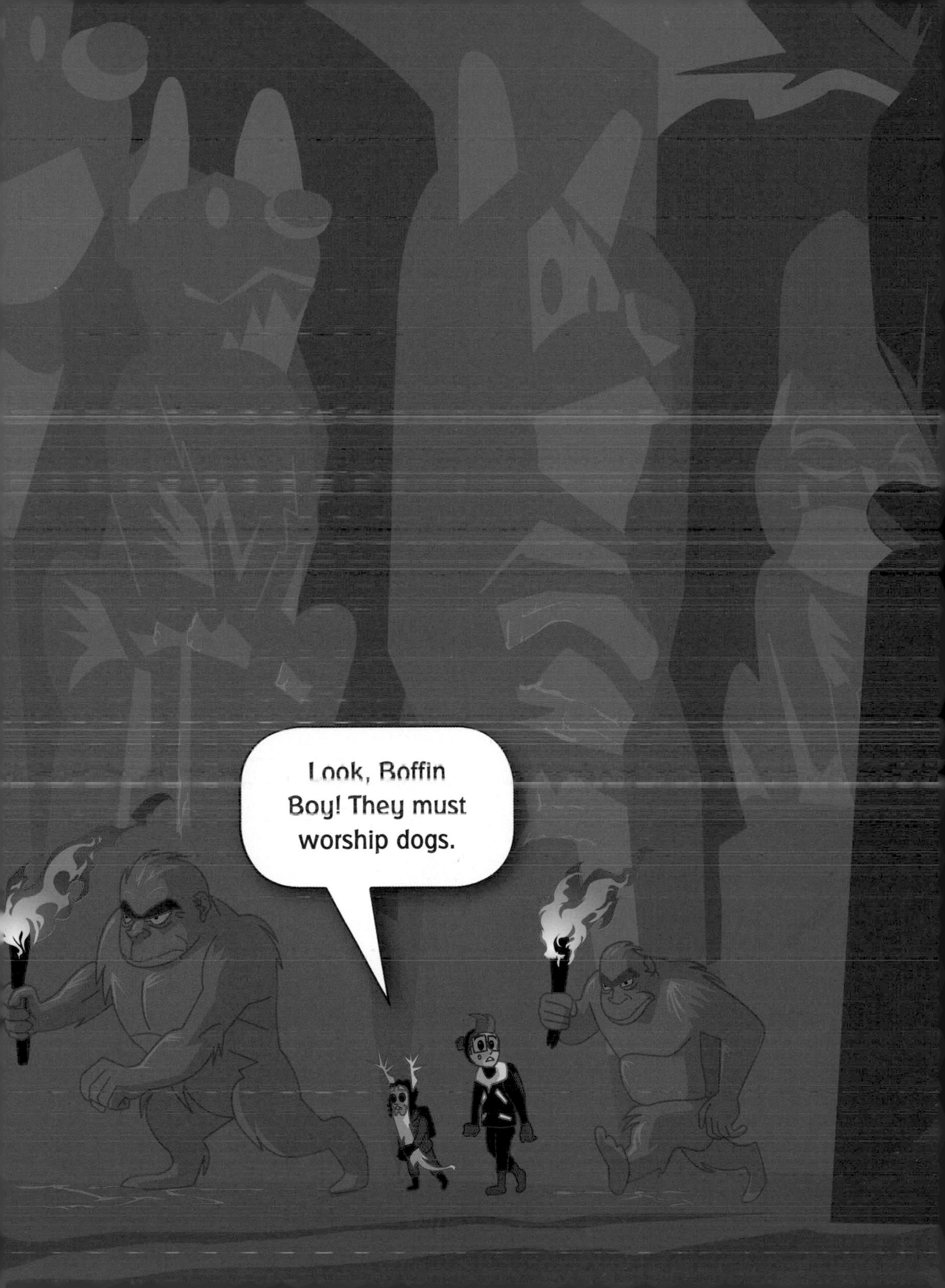
Look, Boffin Boy! They must worship dogs.

Yes!

Er … This isn't Scotland. We're in Tibet. And this is the top of Mount Everest!
Er … Have you got your phone with you, Boffin Boy?

ABOUT THE AUTHOR

David Orme has written well over 200 books including poetry collections, fiction and non-fiction, and school text books. He especially likes writing science fiction stories, and historical stories set in London. Find out more at: www.magic-nation.com.